THE GREAT BIBLE
DISCOVERY

JONAH, JOB, ECCLESIASTES

THE BIBLE IS A BEST-SELLER. IT IS ALSO ONE OF THE MASTER-WORKS OF WORLD LITERATURE - SO IMPORTANT THAT UNIVERSITIES TODAY TEACH 'NON-RELIGIOUS' BIBLE COURSES TO HELP STUDENTS WHO CHOOSE TO STUDY WESTERN LITERATURE.

THE BIBLE POSSESSES AN AMAZING POWER TO FASCINATE YOUNG AND OLD ALIKE.

ONE REASON FOR THIS UNIVERSAL APPEAL IS THAT IT DEALS WITH BASIC HUMAN LONGINGS, EMOTIONS, RELATIONSHIPS. 'ALL THE WORLD IS HERE.' ANOTHER REASON IS THAT SO MUCH OF THE BIBLE CONSISTS OF STORIES. THEY ARE FULL OF MEANING BUT EASY TO REMEMBER.

HERE ARE THOSE STORIES, PRESENTED SIMPLY AND WITH A MINIMUM OF EXPLANATION. WE HAVE LEFT THE TEXT TO SPEAK FOR ITSELF. GIFTED ARTISTS USE THE ACTION-STRIP TECHNIQUE TO BRING THE BIBLE'S DEEP MESSAGE TO READERS OF ALL AGES. THEIR DRAWINGS ARE BASED ON INFORMATION FROM ARCHAEOLOGICAL DISCOVERIES COVERING FIFTEEN CENTURIES.

AN ANCIENT BOOK - PRESENTED FOR THE PEOPLE OF THE SECOND MILLENNIUM. A RELIGIOUS BOOK - PRESENTED FREE FROM THE INTERPRETATION OF ANY PARTICULAR CHURCH. A UNIVERSAL BOOK - PRESENTED IN A FORM THAT ALL MAY ENJOY.

M publishing
CARLISLE, UK

17

The face of the ancient world was transformed by the conquests of Alexander the Great between 334 and 323 BC. Alexander, who was Greek, destroyed the Persian empire and won victories as far east as Afghanistan before he died at Babylon, aged only 33, in 323 BC. He was childless and his empire was divided between his generals. It was because of the Greek influence resulting from this that the New Testament was written in Greek, since this language was understood throughout the Mediterranean and the Near East. It also explains why the Greek translation of the Old Testament became the Bible of the Christian church.

The Jews were affected in many ways. The Old Testament was translated into Greek - at Alexandria, a Greek-speaking city named after Alexander. Many young Jews were attracted by Greek culture and about 175 BC a stadium for Greek sports was built in Jerusalem. Antiochus IV, a descendant of one of Alexander's generals, first appointed a high priest who encouraged the introduction of Greek manners and customs and then turned the Temple itself into a Greek shrine.

For 26 years the sons of a priest called Mattathias, usually known as the Maccabees, fought against their Greek rulers and against the Jews who wanted to adopt Greek ways. The story of these years is told in 1 & 2 Maccabees, which form part of what is often called the Apocrypha, regarded as part of the Bible by some Christians, but not by others.

When the Maccabean forces won victory in 142 BC they achieved independence and for 80 years Judaea was ruled by a succession of priest-kings. But in 64 BC Syria became part of the Roman empire and Judaea found itself once more under foreign rule.

Jonah
Job
Ecclesiastes
1 & 2 Maccabees

JONAH, JOB, ECCLESIASTES

17

First published as *Découvrir la Bible* 1983

First edition © Larousse S.A. 1984
24-volume series adaptation by Mike Jacklin © Knowledge Unlimited 1994
This edition © OM Publishing 1995

01 00 99 98 97 96 95   7 6 5 4 3 2 1

OM Publishing is an imprint of Send the Light Ltd.,
P.O. Box 300, Carlisle, Cumbria CA3 0QS, U.K.

Introductions: Peter Cousins

British Library Cataloguing in Publication Data
A catalogue record for this book is available from the British Library
ISBN 1-85078-221-0

Printed in Singapore by Tien Wah Press (Pte) Ltd.

NINEVEH WAS THE CAPITAL OF THE GREAT ASSYRIAN EMPIRE.

NO ARMY IN THE WORLD WOULD DARE TO ATTACK NINEVEH!

NO! WE'RE AFRAID OF NOTHING AND NO ONE.

JONAH ALSO KNEW WHAT PEOPLE SAID ABOUT THE GREAT CITY...

ARE YOU GOING AWAY, JONAH?

YES, I'M OFF TO JOPPA AND THERE I'LL GET A SHIP TO TARSHISH.

...AND HE DECIDED TO RUN AWAY IN THE OPPOSITE DIRECTION.

JOPPA! NOW ALL I HAVE TO DO IS FIND A SHIP!

ONCE I'M IN TARSHISH, I'LL BE FAR AWAY FROM GOD.

ALL ABOARD! HURRY UP!

CAPTAIN, THE WIND IS GETTING UP!

YES, I'M AFRAID WE'RE IN FOR A STORM...

IN FACT, VERY SOON THE WIND BECAME SO MUCH STRONGER AND THE SEA SO ROUGH THAT THE SHIP WAS IN DANGER OF BREAKING UP.

WIND, CALM YOUR ANGER!

GODS OF THE SEA, HAVE PITY ON US!

WHILE EVERYONE ON DECK WAS TERRIFIED, JONAH WAS SOUND ASLEEP IN THE HOLD...

5

CAPTAIN! LOOK OVER THERE! A SEA-MONSTER!

AND THE MONSTER SWALLOWED JONAH...

IN MY GREAT NEED
I CRIED TO THE LORD,
AND HE ANSWERED ME...
YOU THREW ME DOWN INTO
THE DEPTHS,
TO THE VERY BOTTOM OF THE SEA...
THE GATES OF THE UNDERWORLD
LOCKED ME IN FOR EVER.
BUT, LORD, MY GOD,
YOU BROUGHT ME BACK
ALIVE FROM THE DEPTHS.

JONAH WAS INSIDE THE MONSTER FOR THREE DAYS AND THREE NIGHTS. THEN THE LORD ORDERED IT TO SPIT OUT ITS PRISONER...

THIS TIME I'LL GO TO NINEVEH, AS YOU ASKED ME!

AFTER A VERY LONG JOURNEY...

NINEVEH? RIGHT IN FRONT OF YOU!

THANK YOU, SON.

AND NOW, LORD, HELP ME!

THE LORD SAYS THAT IN 40 DAYS' TIME NINEVEH WILL BE DESTROYED!

...JUST 40 DAYS, AND NINEVEH WILL BE DESTROYED

JONAH WENT UP AND DOWN THE CITY, ANNOUNCING THE TERRIBLE NEWS.

THE PEOPLE OF NINEVEH LISTENED TO THE PROPHET'S MESSAGE.

WE'VE DECIDED TO FAST, AND TO BEG THE LORD, YOUR GOD, TO SPARE US.

EVEN THE KING TOOK THE MATTER VERY SERIOUSLY.

YOUR MAJESTY, THIS MAN REALLY IS A MESSENGER FROM THE GODS.

BUT, IF HE IS SPEAKING THE TRUTH, HOW CAN WE ESCAPE THIS DISASTER?

PROCLAIM A FAST, WHICH EVERY CITIZEN OF NINEVEH MUST KEEP, AND TURN TO GOD.

BEGINNING WITH US!

AND THEY DID SO!

THE FORTIETH DAY DAWNED...

NOW, LORD, LET YOUR ANGER FALL ON THESE PEOPLE!

... BUT NOTHING HAPPENED! THEN...

THE LORD HAS LISTENED TO US!

SAVED! WE'RE SAVED!

FORGIVENESS FOR THESE PAGANS! IS THIS WHY I CAME HERE?

THE NEXT DAY GOD MADE A CASTOR-OIL PLANT GROW, WHICH GAVE JONAH SHADE, AND MADE HIM HAPPY.

JOB LIVED IN THE LAND OF UZ. HE WAS A FINE, HONEST MAN, WHO WORSHIPPED GOD, AND NEVER DID ANYTHING WRONG.

JOB, YOU'VE BECOME THE RICHEST MAN IN THE EAST!

EVEN IF YOU'RE RIGHT, I KNOW THAT I'VE HAD NOTHING TO DO WITH IT... GOD HAS GIVEN IT ALL TO ME.

BUT YOU MUST ADMIT THAT HE HASN'T BEEN STINGY WITH YOU! SEVEN SONS! THOUSANDS OF ANIMALS!

THAT'S ONE THING, MY FRIEND. BUT TO DO GOD'S WILL IS ANOTHER MATTER ALTOGETHER.

HE WAS RIGHT... ONE DAY THE SATAN HIMSELF WENT TO SPEAK TO GOD ABOUT JOB.

HE IS FAITHFUL TO YOU, BECAUSE YOU'VE GIVEN HIM PLENTY! TAKE IT ALL AWAY FROM HIM, AND I'M SURE HE'LL CURSE YOU!

AND THEN?

GOD REPLIED TO THE SATAN: 'DO WHAT YOU LIKE WITH ALL HE HAS...' AND THE SATAN WENT AWAY...

13

14

THEN GOD SAID TO THE SATAN: 'YOU'VE SEEN MY SERVANT JOB! IN SPITE OF ALL THAT HAS HAPPENED TO HIM, HE IS AS FAITHFUL TO ME AS EVER!'

THE SATAN REPLIED: 'THAT'S BECAUSE HE WANTS TO STAY ALIVE MORE THAN ANYTHING ELSE! LET ME HURT HIS BODY, AND YOU'LL SEE!'

...AND TERRIBLE SORES BROKE OUT ALL OVER JOB'S BODY.

YOU POOR MAN! YOU WOULD DO BETTER TO CURSE GOD, AND DIE!

WIFE, BE QUIET!

WE WERE GLAD OF THE GOOD TIMES GOD SENT. SHALL WE REFUSE TO ACCEPT THE BAD?

WELL, HERE ARE YOUR FRIENDS, COME TO SHARE YOUR BAD LUCK.

15

JOB'S THREE FRIENDS WERE ELIPHAZ, BILDAD, AND ZOPHAR. FOR 7 DAYS NO ONE SAID A WORD. THEN JOB BEGAN TO COMPLAIN...

CURSE THE DAY I WAS BORN! I WISH I HAD DIED IN MY MOTHER'S WOMB. THEN TODAY I WOULD BE SLEEPING QUIETLY WITH THE DEAD.

COME ON, JOB! YOU USED TO GIVE OTHER PEOPLE STRENGTH; NOW YOU'RE THE ONE WHO IS WEAK!

IF I WERE YOU, I WOULD TURN TO GOD! THINK YOURSELF LUCKY TO BE PUNISHED LIKE THIS! GOD WOUNDS US, AND HE HEALS US!

ELIPHAZ! IS THAT HOW YOU COMFORT ME? WHY SHOULD I BE PUNISHED? I'VE NEVER BROKEN GOD'S COMMANDMENTS!

O MY GOD! WHAT HAVE I DONE TO YOU?

16

THAT'S ENOUGH! ARE YOU GOING TO ACCUSE GOD OF NOT BEING FAIR? IF HE STRIKES YOU, IT'S BECAUSE YOU DESERVE IT. LOOK AT WHAT HE DID TO YOUR SONS; THEY DIDN'T ALWAYS BEHAVE PROPERLY!

IS ANYONE GOOD IN GOD'S SIGHT?

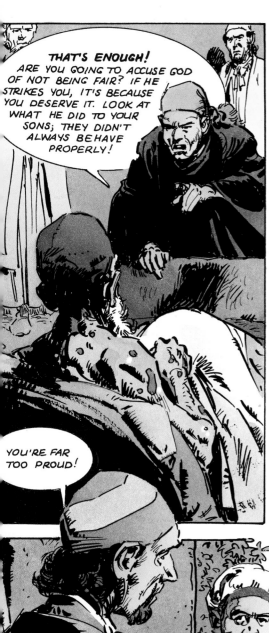

YOU'RE FAR TOO PROUD!

BUT I'M INNOCENT! AND GOD IS DESTROYING ME AS IF I WERE GUILTY!

ZOPHAR, IT IS YOUR TURN.

ADMIT THAT YOU'LL NEVER UNDERSTAND GOD'S WISDOM! HAVE DONE WITH EVIL AND WRONG, AND YOU'LL BE AT PEACE.

18

In the wisdom literature found in the bible this is one of the best known books. It is a rich collection of jewish wisdom. At one time many believed that the great King Solomon had written it. The real author humbly calls himself Ecclesiastes ('the preacher'), in hebrew:

QOHELETH

WHAT A JOY FOR OUR FAMILY!

LIFE! WHAT A WONDERFUL THING!

BUT NOTHING IS SADDER THAN A BIRTH!

WHY DO YOU SAY THAT?

WHEN YOU'RE BORN, YOU BEGIN TO DIE! WE SHOULD WEEP FOR THE NEW-BORN, AND HAVE A PARTY FOR THE ONE WHO DIES.

YOU MAY ASK THESE QUESTIONS, BUT YOU DON'T HAVE THE RIGHT TO STOP THERE...

DO YOU KNOW THE WISDOM OF SOLOMON? COME, I'LL TAKE YOU TO HIS TABLE, AND SOMETHING TELLS ME THAT YOU'LL SATISFY YOUR HUNGER THERE...

21

THIS IS HOW IT IS... IN THIS LIFE THERE IS A TIME FOR EVERYTHING...

COME!

A TIME TO BE BORN, A TIME TO DIE, A TIME TO PLANT, A TIME TO DIG UP, A TIME TO LOVE, A TIME TO HATE...

ONLY WHAT GOD DOES LASTS FOR EVER. YOU CAN'T ADD ANYTHING TO IT OR TAKE ANYTHING AWAY FROM IT.

BUT...?

LOOK WHAT GOD HAS DONE. HOW CAN ANYONE STRAIGHTEN WHAT HE HAS MADE CROOKED?

ON THE GOOD DAY BE HAPPY, AND ON THE BAD DAY STOP AND THINK, BECAUSE GOD MADE BOTH OF THEM.

23

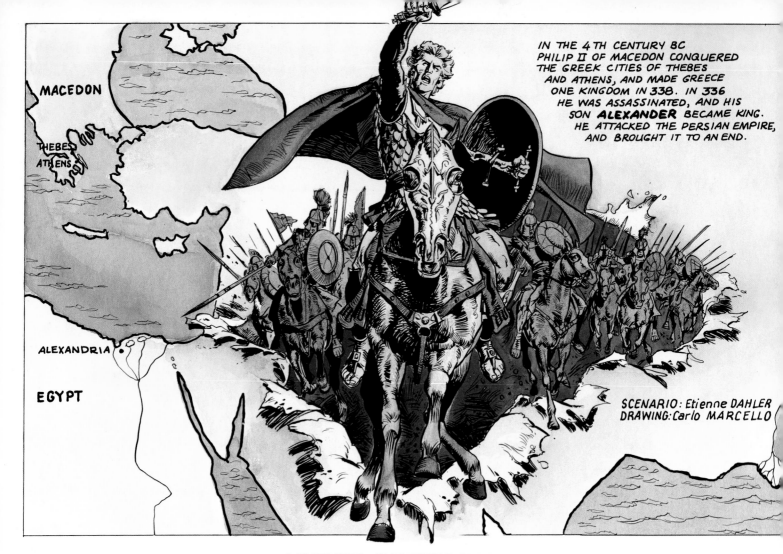

IN THE 4TH CENTURY BC PHILIP II OF MACEDON CONQUERED THE GREEK CITIES OF THEBES AND ATHENS, AND MADE GREECE ONE KINGDOM IN 338. IN 336 HE WAS ASSASSINATED, AND HIS SON **ALEXANDER** BECAME KING. HE ATTACKED THE PERSIAN EMPIRE, AND BROUGHT IT TO AN END.

MACEDON

THEBES
ATHENS

ALEXANDRIA

EGYPT

SCENARIO: Etienne DAHLER
DRAWING: Carlo MARCELLO

UNDER GREEK RULE

THE REVOLT OF THE MACCABEES

BY WINNING ONE BATTLE AFTER ANOTHER, ALEXANDER'S ARMY WAS SOON NEAR TO SAMARIA. IN 332 THE GOVERNOR OF THE CITY CAME TO MEET HIM IN TYRE.

SIRE, MY PROVINCE SUBMITS TO YOU.

GOOD! THAT SAVES ME FROM HAVING TO GO OUT OF MY WAY.

THEN MAY I DARE TO ASK YOU TO ALLOW US TO BUILD A TEMPLE ON MOUNT GERIZIM...

GRANTED! IN EXCHANGE GIVE ME 8 000 OF YOUR MEN TO ATTACK EGYPT!

IN EGYPT THE GOVERNOR GAVE IN WITHOUT A FIGHT, AND THE PEOPLE WELCOMED THEIR LIBERATOR. *

LONG LIVE ALEXANDER!

DOWN WITH THE PERSIANS!

BE OUR KING!

*Egypt had been ruled by Persia since 525 BC.

BUT NOT ALL THE PEOPLE EVERYWHERE WERE SO HAPPY. SAMARIA ROSE UP AGAINST ITS NEW GREEK GOVERNOR, ANDROMACHOS, AND KILLED HIM.

DOWN WITH THE TYRANTS!

MEANWHILE ALEXANDER WANTED TO BUILD A NEW CITY IN EGYPT...

IT MUST BE BUILT HERE, BETWEEN THE SEA AND THE LAKE.

...A CITY WHICH WOULD BECOME ONE OF THE MOST IMPORTANT IN THE MEDITERRANEAN WORLD: ALEXANDRIA.

THE EGYPTIAN PEOPLE ARE VERY PEACEFUL.

I'M NOT NEEDED HERE ANY LONGER... THERE ARE OTHER CAMPAIGNS WAITING FOR ME.

27

IN 331 BC ALEXANDER CAPTURED THE PERSIAN CAPITALS. THEN HE SET OUT ON AN ENORMOUS EXPEDITION, WHICH TOOK HIM AS FAR AS THE RIVER INDUS.

SIRE, THE MEN HAVE HAD ENOUGH. THEY REFUSE TO GO ANY FURTHER.

THEN I MUST RETURN TO BABYLON...

WHEN HE ARRIVED BACK, ALEXANDER WAS ANXIOUS TO BIND HIS HUGE EMPIRE TOGETHER...

STATIRA AND PARYSATIS, YOU'LL BE MY PERSIAN WIVES. THE PEOPLE ARE WITNESSES TO IT.

IN THE YEAR 323...

THE FEVER IS KILLING ME... HOLD ME UP... CALL MY GENERALS.

MY FRIENDS, I'M AFRAID I'LL SOON BE LEAVING YOU... AND... I WANT TO SHARE OUT MY KINGDOM...

A WISE THING TO DO... EVEN THOUGH IT DIDN'T STOP HIS GENERALS FROM FIERCELY ATTACKING ONE ANOTHER AFTER HIS DEATH.

SOON THE GROUPS WERE LOCKED IN BATTLE: THE PTOLEMIES OF EGYPT AND THE SELEUCIDS OF SYRIA.

SYRIA

ALEXANDRIA

EGYPT

JUDAEA AND SAMARIA, WHICH LAY BETWEEN THE TWO ENEMIES, WOULD SUFFER TERRIBLY...

FROM 321 BC THE PTOLEMIES OF EGYPT WERE IN CONTROL...

THE JEWS ARE CELEBRATING THE SABBATH. EVERYONE STAYS AT HOME. THERE ARE ONLY A FEW SENTRIES...

WE WON'T LET THIS CHANCE SLIP BY... ATTACK!

AND JERUSALEM FELL INTO THE HANDS OF PTOLEMY I, THE FUTURE KING OF EGYPT. HE SENT MANY OF ITS PEOPLE INTO EXILE IN ALEXANDRIA.

COME ON! HURRY UP!

NO NEED TO SHOW THEM THE WAY TO EGYPT! THEY KNOW IT WELL!

WITHIN 50 YEARS THE JEWISH COMMUNITY IN ALEXANDRIA HAD BECOME VERY IMPORTANT. THE NEW KING, PTOLEMY II, TREATED THEM WELL.

ALL THE JEWS IN THE ARMY OR WHO WORK FOR OTHER PEOPLE ARE SET FREE!

IN ALEXANDRIA, AROUND THE YEAR 230 BC, 70 JEWS TRANSLATED THEIR SACRED WRITINGS FROM HEBREW INTO GREEK.

PTOLEMY II WANTS TO GIVE OUR TORAH A SPECIAL PLACE IN HIS LIBRARY...

...AND OUR BROTHERS ALL OVER THE GREEK WORLD WILL NOW BE ABLE TO READ IT IN THE LANGUAGE THEY SPEAK EVERY DAY...

...WHICH HAPPENED IN ANTIOCH, IN EPHESUS...

FROM NOW ON WE'LL READ THE SCRIPTURES FROM THE SEPTUAGINT* TEXT.

* The name given to the Greek translation.

FOR THE FIRST TIME THE SACRED WRITINGS WERE BROUGHT TOGETHER UNDER ONE NAME: BIBLIA.*

*In Greek, 'books'.

BUT IN JERUSALEM THE JEWS WERE NOT HAPPY ABOUT IT...

NOTHING CAN TAKE THE PLACE OF GOD'S LANGUAGE! HOW COULD THOSE JEWS HAVE MADE SUCH A MISTAKE?

THE COMPLAINTS DIED DOWN ...CE A NEW DANGER ...REATENED.

THIS HAS BEEN GOING ON TOO LONG! WILL THEY NEVER STOP KILLING ONE ANOTHER?

IT SEEMS THAT THE SELEUCIDS OF SYRIA ARE ON THEIR WAY TO JERUSALEM.

31

IN FACT, A LITTLE LATER, IN JERUSALEM...

THE KING OF THE SELEUCIDS IS HERE, WITH HIS WHOLE ARMY!

OPEN THE GATES FOR ANTIOCHUS! DON'T TRY TO STOP HIM!

THAT WAS HOW PALESTINE AND JERUSALEM PASSED INTO THE HANDS OF THE SELEUCIDS.

I, ANTIOCHUS III, ORDER THAT ALL JEWS HELD AS SLAVES ARE TO BE SET FREE... WHAT IS MORE...

...ALL JEWS MAY LIVE ACCORDING TO THEIR LAW, AND I EXCUSE THE OLD PEOPLE AND THE PRIESTS FROM PAYING TAXES.

SO, AS THE SECOND CENTURY BC BEGAN, JERUSALEM WAS A SPLENDID CITY AGAIN. ONE WISE MAN WAS AMAZED TO SEE IT: JESUS BEN* SIRACH.

* Son of

AT THE TEMPLE IN JERUSALEM...

THE HIGH PRIEST SIMON WILL SEE YOU NOW...

SIMON!

BEN SIRACH! I'M SO HAPPY TO SEE YOU AGAIN!

THE WISDOM OF BEN SIRACH IS FOUND IN THE BOOK OF ECCLESIASTICUS.

I'VE BROUGHT YOU MY NEWEST SCROLL.

I'M LISTENING...

THE WISE MAN READ IT TO HIS FRIEND...

THE LORD MADE PEOPLE FROM THE GROUND AND HE MAKES THEM GO BACK TO IT.

GOD HAS GIVEN YOU WISDOM. YOU MUST TEACH IT.

FOR THE JEWS THESE GOOD TIMES WOULD SOON COME TO AN END. IN ANTIOCH, IN SYRIA, A TYRANT CAME TO POWER IN 175 BC; **ANTIOCHUS IV EPIPHANES.**

WHAT IS HE GOING TO DO?

WE MUST EXPECT THE WORST!

THOSE WHO DON'T OBEY WILL BE CRUSHED!

WHEN ONIAS, THE HIGH PRIEST, WENT TO ANTIOCH, HIS BROTHER JASON SAW HIS CHANCE, AND TOOK HIS PLACE...

JASON, THE KING IS COUNTING ON YOU TO PERSUADE THE JEWISH PEOPLE.

HE WAS IN FAVOUR OF GREEK CUSTOMS, EVEN IF THEY WERE AGAINST THE LAW.

MANY PEOPLE QUICKLY ACCEPTED THE GREEK WAYS.

WHAT A DISGRACE! ISRAEL LEARNING FROM THE GREEKS!

A GYMNASIUM... WHERE THEY GET US TO ALL SORTS OF STRANGE THINGS

THE YOUNG JEWS WERE NOT COMPLAINING!

I THINK I'M FIT FOR THE NEXT GAMES IN TYRE!

JASON WOULDN'T BENEFIT FROM THIS SITUATION FOR VERY LONG. THREE YEARS LATER...

MENELAUS, I TRUST YOU FULLY. TAKE THIS YEAR'S TRIBUTE TO THE KING IN ANTIOCH.

DON'T WORRY, JASON, I'LL DO WHAT YOU ASK AS IF I WERE DOING IT FOR MYSELF.

NOW THEN, MENELAUS, WHY DO YOU HOPE THAT THE KING WILL MAKE YOU HIGH PRIEST IN JASON'S PLACE?

BECAUSE I'LL GIVE HIM MORE MONEY THAN JASON.

[ME]NELAUS WAS RIGHT. [WH]EN JASON HEARD [TH]E NEWS IN [JE]RUSALEM...

THE TRAITOR! I'LL BE BACK! AND MY REVENGE WILL BE TERRIBLE!

HE FLED ACROSS THE RIVER JORDAN.

[S]ON MENELAUS BECAME VERY [UN]POPULAR.

[H]E HAS DARED TO SELL [TH]E HOLY VESSELS FROM THE TEMPLE!

THE LORD WILL PUNISH HIM!

MEANWHILE ANTIOCHUS EPIPHANES WAS WAGING WAR IN EGYPT...

SUDDENLY A PIECE OF NEWS SHOOK THE WHOLE KINGDOM...

ANTIOCHUS EPIPHANES HAS BEEN KILLED IN BATTLE!

FATHER, A NEW GROUP JOINED US THIS MORNING.

NOW THERE ARE NEARLY 6000 OF US!

THE FAITHFUL PEOPLE! *

*In Hebrew, chasîdîm.

THE REBELS MADE MORE AND MORE ATTACKS.

WE'RE READY TO DIE FOR THE LAW!

IN 166 B.C., A YEAR AFTER THE REVOLT BEGAN, MATTATHIAS FELT HE WAS GROWING WEAKER...

MY FRIENDS, MY SON SIMON IS A WISE MAN. LISTEN TO HIM. HE'LL BE A FATHER TO YOU.

AND YOU, JUDAS MACCABAEUS, YOU'LL COMMAND THE ARMY.

FATHER, I PROMISE YOU THAT I'LL PAY THE NATIONS BACK FOR THE WRONG THEY'VE DONE TO US!

TWO GENERALS, NICANOR AND GORGIAS, MARCHED ON JUDAEA AT THE HEAD OF A HUGE ARMY.

I'VE CALLED THE SLAVE-TRADERS TOGETHER... I'LL SOON BE SELLING THEM THOUSANDS OF JEWS!

YOU ALWAYS DID HAVE A HEAD FOR BUSINESS, NICANOR!

MEANWHILE JUDAS MACCABAEUS ASSEMBLED HIS TROOPS AT MIZPAH.

WE'VE FASTED AND PRAYED. NOW MAY GOD GIVE US VICTORY... OR DEATH!

FOR TORAH AND TEMPLE!

GORGIAS IS COMING TO MEET US WITH 5000 MEN!

PERFECT! WHILE HE'S SEARCHING FOR US, WE'LL ATTACK HIS CAMP AT EMMAUS.

THE REBELS SURPRISED THE CAMP. SO THEY WERE ABLE TO WIPE OUT THE ARMY OF NICANOR, WHO WAS KILLED DURING THE BATTLE.

NOW FOR JERUSALEM!

42

THE MACCABEES WENT ON FIGHTING. SIMON FROM GALILEE TO ACCO, JUDAS IN GILEAD, THEN IN IDUMAEA. HE CAPTURED HEBRON. IN PHILISTIA HE ATTACKED ASHDOD.

Acco
Mediterranean Sea
GALILEE
GILEAD
JERUSALEM
Dead Sea
HEBRON
PHILISTIA
ASHDOD
IDUMAEA

ANTIOCHUS V REACTED VIOLENTLY. HE WAS BESIEGING THE TEMPLE IN JERUSALEM, WHEN NEWS ARRIVED.

PHILIP * HAS CAPTURED ANTIOCH!

WE MUST GO BACK. A PITY ABOUT THE MACCABEES!

* Regent of the kingdom during the campaigns.

ANTIOCHUS V DEFEATED PHILIP, BUT WAS MURDERED SOON AFTERWARDS BY HIS COUSIN DEMETRIUS. THE NEW KING CARRIED ON THE FIGHT AGAINST THE JEWS, WHO WERE LOSING HEART...

OUR REVOLT WAS GOING WELL. WE DEFEATED NICANOR. BUT THIS TIME...

JERUSALEM IS LOST! EVERYTHING IS LOST!

JUDAS, MANY OF OUR PEOPLE HAVE RUN AWAY. WE CAN'T STAND UP TO 20 000 MEN!

DON'T YOU LEAVE. IF OUR TIME HAS COME, WE'LL DIE FOR OUR BROTHERS!

IN APRIL–MAY 160 B C, WITH 800 BRAVE MEN, JUDAS WENT INTO BATTLE. TOWARDS EVENING...

JUDAS, FOR TORAH AND TEMPLE!

AAAH!... MY GOD!

A FEW MONTHS LATER...

THE UNGODLY RULE OVER THE WHOLE OF JUDAEA AGAIN! WE CAN'T HAVE THAT!

THE ROMANS WILL HELP US...

JONATHAN, TAKE THE PLACE OF YOUR BROTHER, JUDAS.

VERY WELL! WITH THE LORD WE'LL FREE OUR LAND!

JONATHAN WON MANY VICTORIES, AND GRADUALLY GAINED CONTROL OF JUDAEA.

WHY IS DEMETRIUS LETTING US DO THIS WITHOUT MAKING ANY MOVE?

HE HAS OTHER WORRIES... BALAS, THE SON OF ANTIOCHUS EPIPHANES, IS CLAIMING THE THRONE, AND REBELLING AGAINST HIM.

JONATHAN HELPED THE REBELS WHO WERE FIGHTING KING DEMETRIUS...

BALAS, I'M ON YOUR SIDE, WITH ALL MY MEN!

JONATHAN, I APPOINT YOU HIGH PRIEST IN JERUSALEM.

AS THE YEARS PASSED, THERE WAS ONE GREEK KING AFTER ANOTHER, BUT JONATHAN WAS CLEVER ENOUGH TO MAKE EACH ONE DEPEND ON HIM. SOON HE WAS CIVIL AND MILITARY GOVERNOR OF JUDAEA, WHICH HAD DOUBLED IN SIZE!

DEAD SEA

JERUSALEM

ASCALON

GAZA

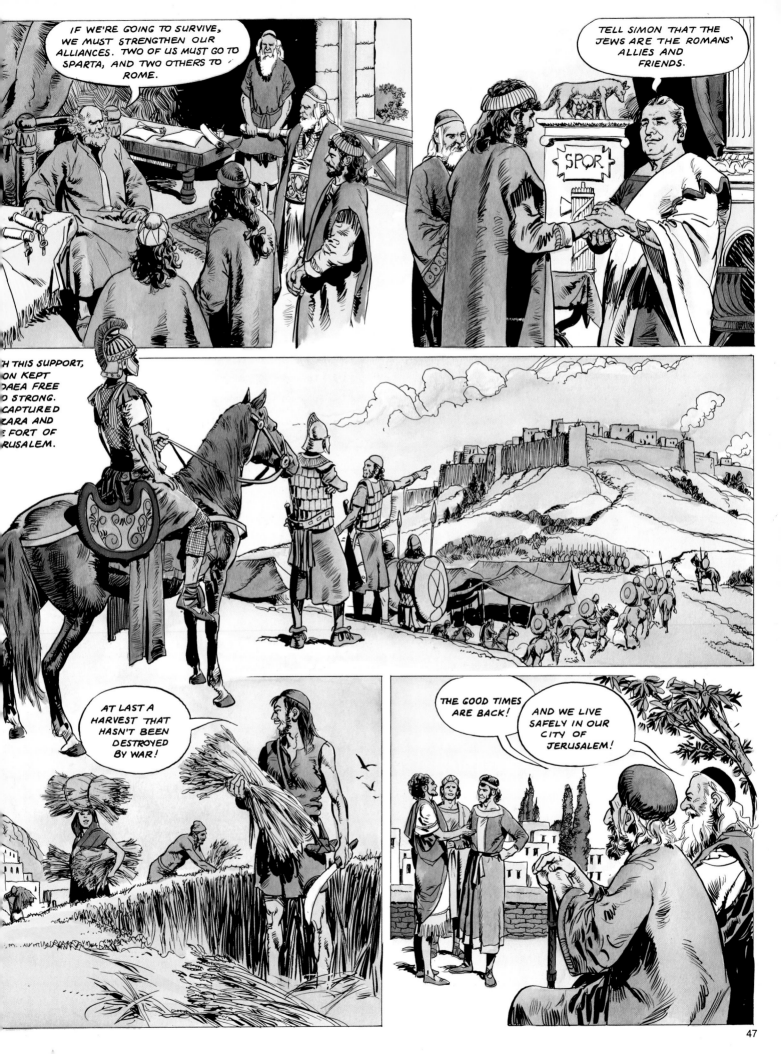

47

JUDAEA WAS COMPLETELY INDEPENDENT WHEN, IN 134 B.C, SIMON WAS MURDERED BY HIS OWN SON-IN-LAW AT JERICHO.

HIS SON, **JOHN HYRCANUS**, WAS PROCLAIMED HIGH PRIEST AND ETHNARCH* IN JERUSALEM.

MY FATHER WILL BE AVENGED. AND WE SHALL STAND FIRM!

THE JEWISH STATE, RESTORED BY MATTATHIAS AND HIS SONS, LASTED UNTIL A.D 70.

* Governor.

GALILEE

SEPPHORIS

DOR

GADARA

PELLA

SAMARIA

APOLLONIA

JUDAEA

JERICHO

JOPPA

MEDABA

JERUSALEM

HEBRON

Dead Sea